SECRET OF WHITE MONKS ABBEY

PHILIP HERRIOTT

First published in 1985 by Macmillan Children's Books a division of Macmillan Publishers Ltd. London and Basingstoke

ISBN 0 333 38893 3 HB ISBN 0 333 38894 1 PB
Magic Mystery Books are produced by Mushroom Books Ltd. 9 Newburgh Street London W1V 1LH
Origination by Newsele S.R.L. (UK) 01·734 0628 Printed in Italy in association with Keats European Ltd.

MAGIC MYSTERY CLUB

Calling the hawk-eyed, cunning and sharp-witted. Join the Magic Mystery Club! You will receive a Special Investigator's pack containing: a Magic Mystery Club badge, personalised I.D. card, code maker/breaker kit and a top secret document.

All you have to do is write your age and your name and address in BLOCK CAPITALS on a piece of paper and send it, with a postal order for 50p to:

YM3431
9 Newburgh Street, London W1V 1LH.

Open to residents of the UK and Republic of Ireland only.

Find the clues, solve the mystery and and make a different story every time.

When you read, "Go to the police station on page 2. Or enter the Abbey on page 6.", *you* have to decide what to do, then turn to the page you have chosen. It might be ahead, or it might be behind.

Use your skill to make the right choice. If you are hawk-eyed, cunning and sharp-witted, you'll spot the clues, outwit the enemies and uncover the secret. But the *Magic Mystery* doesn't end there. Each story has more than one ending. Some routes lead to success: on some pages you'll catch the villain. Other routes lead to failure: on some pages the villain will catch you! Whatever happens, remember – find the clues, solve the mystery – and make a different story every time.

Solve the mystery of WHITE MONKS ABBEY

One Summer, you and a friend discover a secret clearing in a tangled thicket deep in White Monks Wood. The clearing is surrounded by dense thorn bushes. Beyond the bushes lies the mysterious White Monks Abbey.

White Monks Abbey is a sinister place. The last owner, a recluse, died ten years ago and the Abbey has been empty since then. The local people are terrified of the place. They tell stories of phantom monks, unearthly noises and flickering lights. They say that the grounds are too overgrown with brambles for anyone to enter – but that's not true – and if you would like to explore White Monks Abbey, read on . . .

1

Waiting in the clearing for your friend, Pat, you notice a strange thing. There is a gaping hole in the thorn hedge, as if someone has pushed through.

Squeeze through the gap and find your way through the trees to the Abbey on page 14. ☞

Or look down at your feet and see another strange thing. A young beech sapling seems to have turned back to front.

You have been keeping a protective eye on the tree for weeks. You know every bud, every leaf. That young branch was on the left yesterday and that brownish leaf was definitely on the right. Could someone have uprooted the tree and replanted it the wrong way? Why?

Stooping to examine the tree, you stumble, and fall onto it. You lift the roots – and the ground follows! You peer into a deep hole where a flight of steps leads into a dark tunnel.

Follow the steps to page 15. ☞

You burst through the doors of White Monks Police Station and gasp your story to the desk sergeant.

To your surprise, he doesn't laugh, or think you're mad, or threaten to tell your parents. He simply asks, "Have you any proof?"

You show him your evidence.

"Right!" he says. "Stay here while I phone headquarters." He's soon back, with two plainclothes policemen. "You've done well," one says. "Now you can leave it to us."

Leave your evidence with the police and go home. Or, if you want to see the adventure through to its end, guide the police through White Monks Wood to the Abbey.

Go to page 8.

3

The most horrible din, like a million school dinner bells, screeches through the tunnel, echoing between the narrow walls. Stale air brushes your cheek, warning you of something moving. Steel glints in the dim light: a shutter is falling behind you! It's going to seal the tunnel. You'll be trapped.

You have about ten seconds. If you're good at gym, snap into action. Roll under the shutter and escape from the tunnel to page 14. ☛

Or wait to see what will happen. Go to page 18. ☛

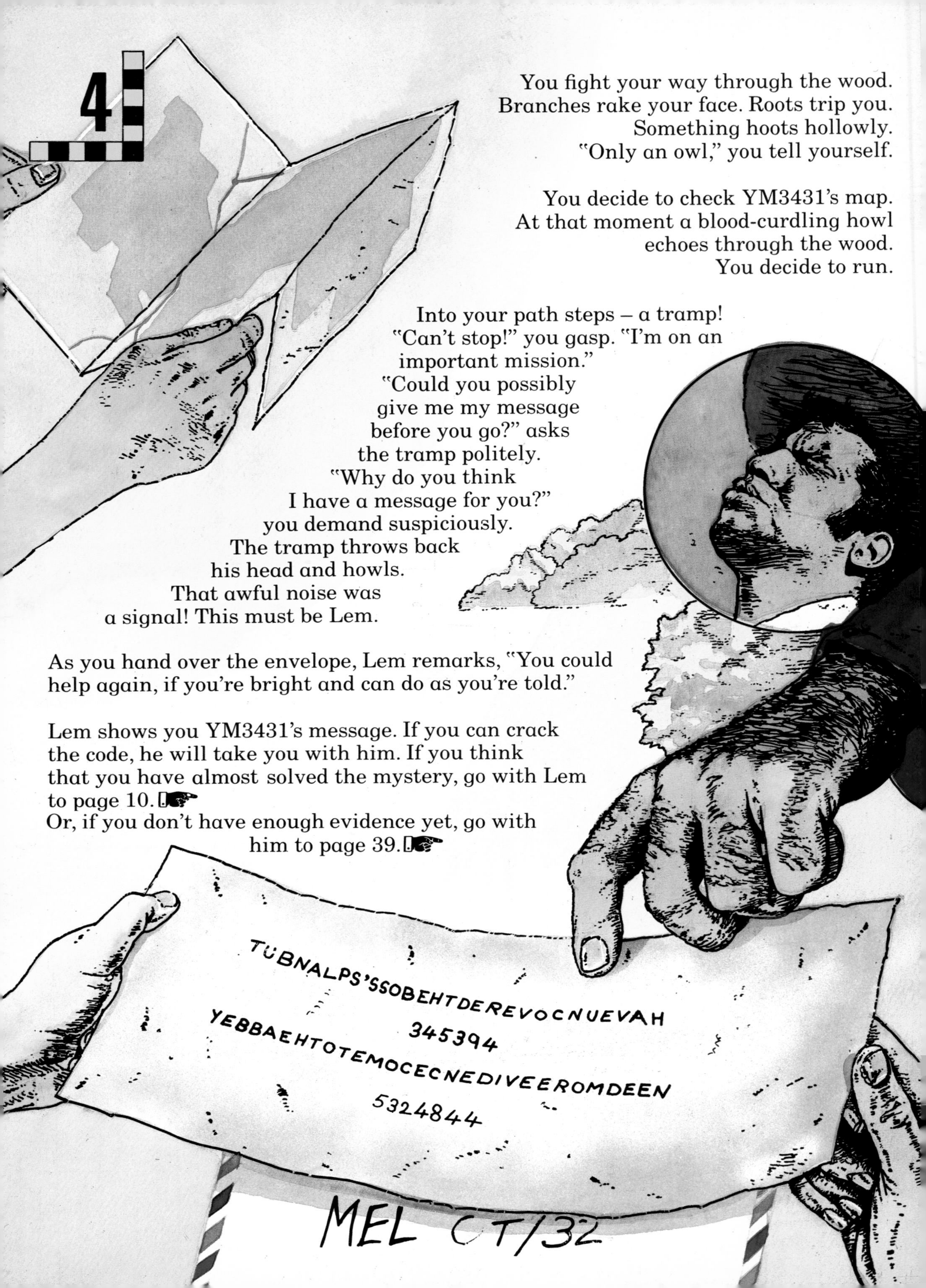

You fight your way through the wood. Branches rake your face. Roots trip you. Something hoots hollowly. "Only an owl," you tell yourself.

You decide to check YM3431's map. At that moment a blood-curdling howl echoes through the wood. You decide to run.

Into your path steps – a tramp! "Can't stop!" you gasp. "I'm on an important mission." "Could you possibly give me my message before you go?" asks the tramp politely. "Why do you think I have a message for you?" you demand suspiciously. The tramp throws back his head and howls. That awful noise was a signal! This must be Lem.

As you hand over the envelope, Lem remarks, "You could help again, if you're bright and can do as you're told."

Lem shows you YM3431's message. If you can crack the code, he will take you with him. If you think that you have almost solved the mystery, go with Lem to page 10.

Or, if you don't have enough evidence yet, go with him to page 39.

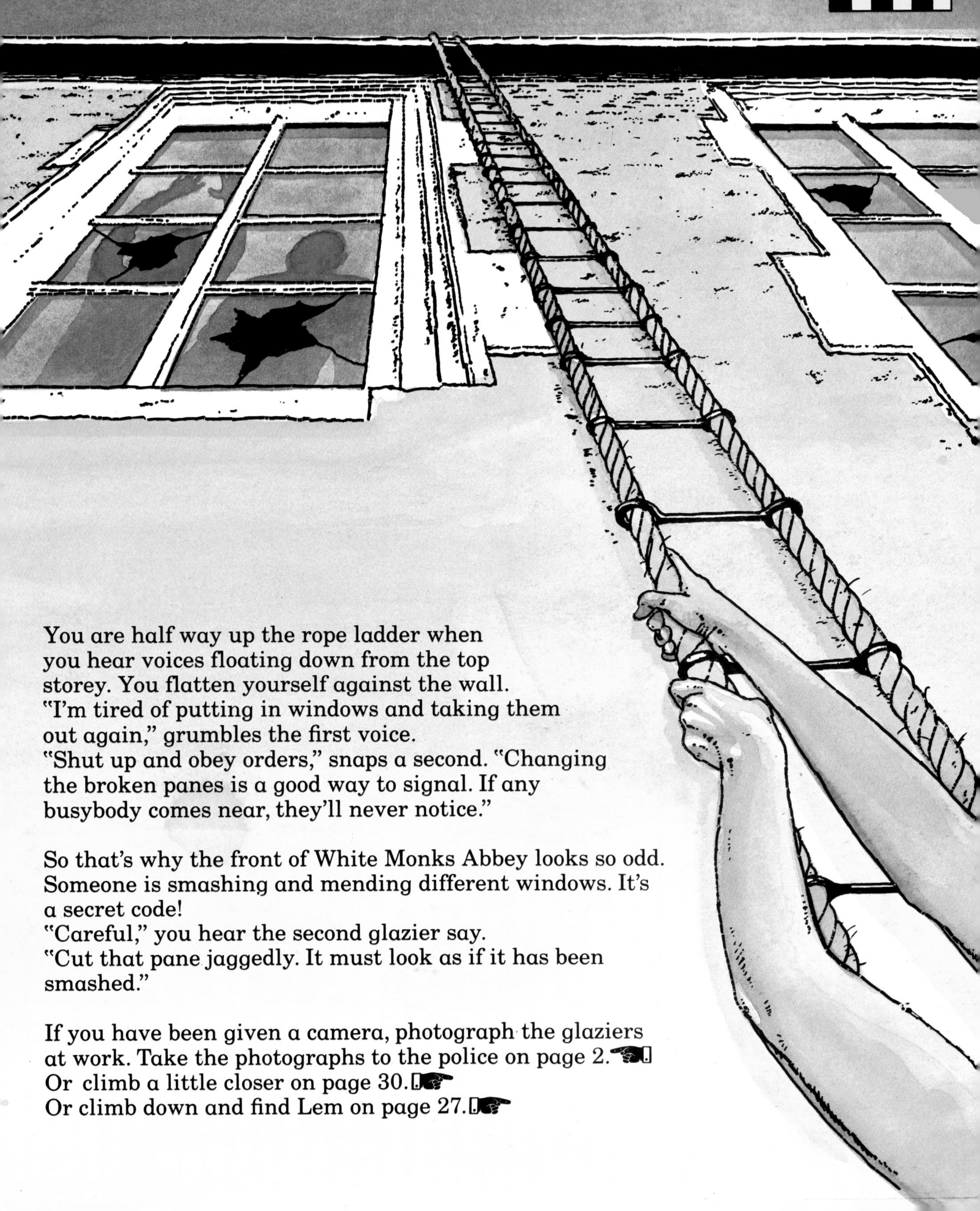

You are half way up the rope ladder when you hear voices floating down from the top storey. You flatten yourself against the wall.
"I'm tired of putting in windows and taking them out again," grumbles the first voice.
"Shut up and obey orders," snaps a second. "Changing the broken panes is a good way to signal. If any busybody comes near, they'll never notice."

So that's why the front of White Monks Abbey looks so odd. Someone is smashing and mending different windows. It's a secret code!
"Careful," you hear the second glazier say.
"Cut that pane jaggedly. It must look as if it has been smashed."

If you have been given a camera, photograph the glaziers at work. Take the photographs to the police on page 2.
Or climb a little closer on page 30.
Or climb down and find Lem on page 27.

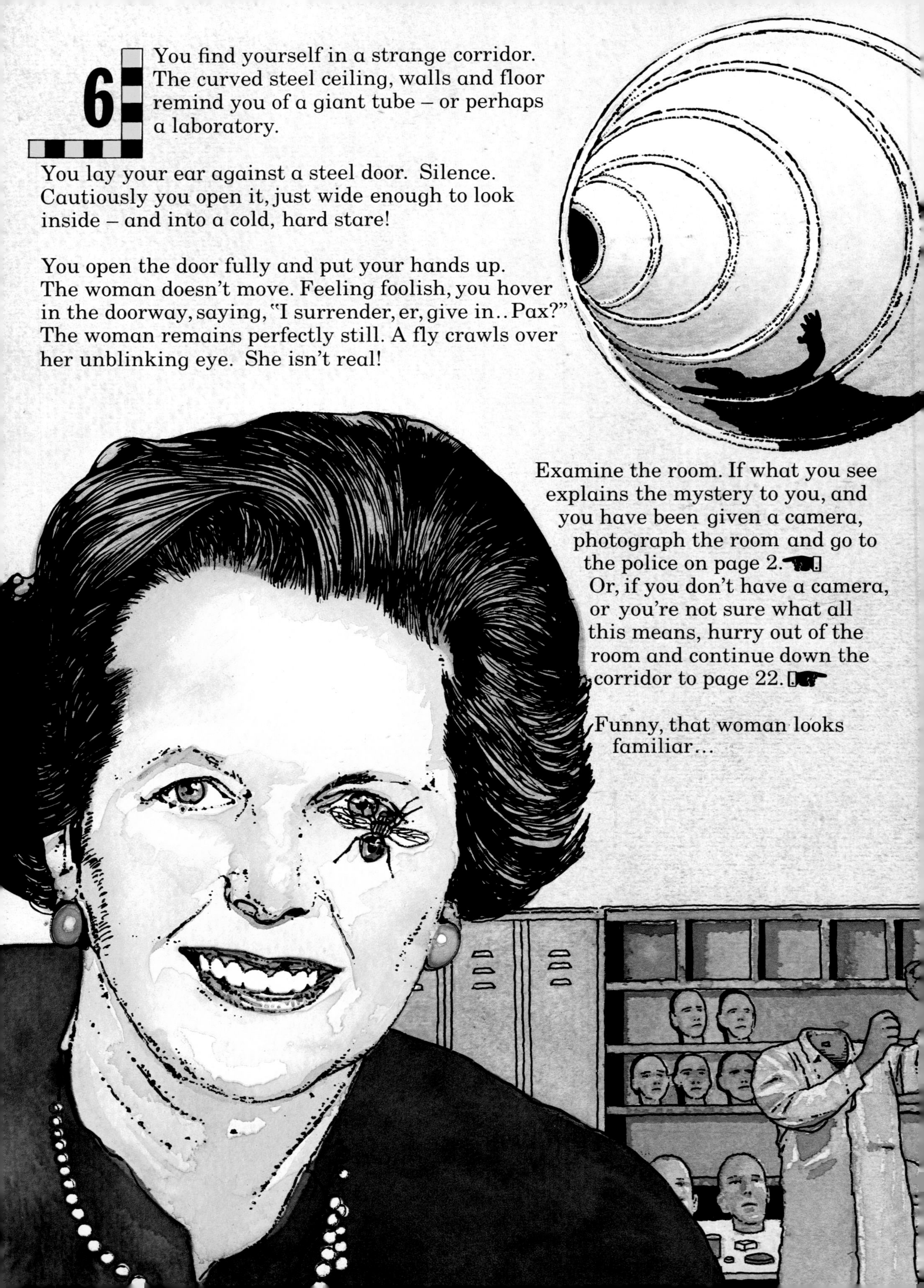

6

You find yourself in a strange corridor. The curved steel ceiling, walls and floor remind you of a giant tube – or perhaps a laboratory.

You lay your ear against a steel door. Silence. Cautiously you open it, just wide enough to look inside – and into a cold, hard stare!

You open the door fully and put your hands up. The woman doesn't move. Feeling foolish, you hover in the doorway, saying, "I surrender, er, give in.. Pax?" The woman remains perfectly still. A fly crawls over her unblinking eye. She isn't real!

Examine the room. If what you see explains the mystery to you, and you have been given a camera, photograph the room and go to the police on page 2.
Or, if you don't have a camera, or you're not sure what all this means, hurry out of the room and continue down the corridor to page 22.

Funny, that woman looks familiar...

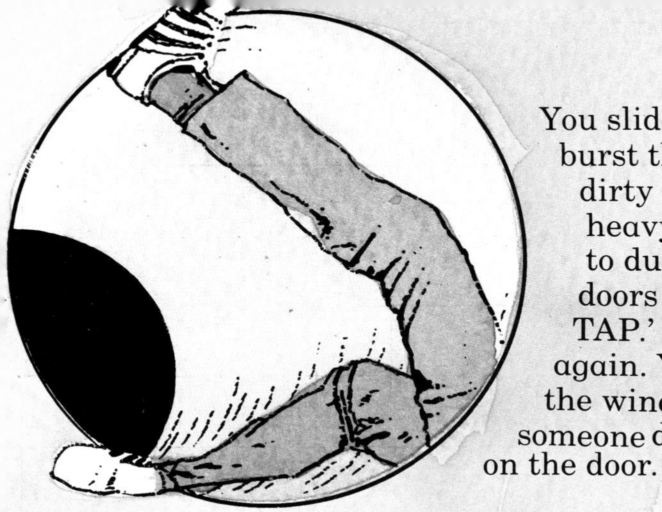

You slide down the slippery chute and burst through a flap, landing on a cold, dirty stone floor. Ahead are several heavy, studded doors. Could they lead to dungeons? From behind one of the doors comes a 'tap, tap, tap-tap, tappity TAP.' You listen. The tapping starts again. Yes, there is a pattern. It's not the wind, or water dripping, but someone drumming on the door.

If Lem is with you, go to page 9.
Or, if Lem isn't with you, try to tap a message back in the same rhythm. Go to page 18.

8

The police reinforcements arrive in an ear-splitting din of screeching brakes and screaming sirens. They hack through the thorn bushes. Some run to block the secret exits, others search the Abbey. Two plainclothes policemen frog-march a raging, hysterical figure to a waiting helicopter. One of them turns to you.

"Well done!" he exclaims. "We've been after the 'Boss' for months; ever since Interpol informed us that he had kidnapped a certain head of state – and replaced him with a robot double! Thanks to you he'll soon be behind bars!"

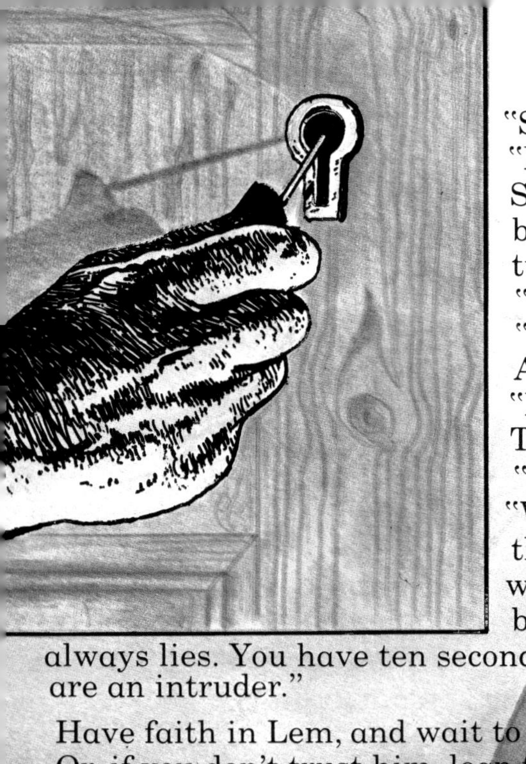

"Soon have this lock picked," mutters Lem. "If only I had some light."
Suddenly the lock is illuminated by a blue beam, coming from the eyes of two identical young men!
"Why are you breaking in?" demands the first twin. "If you are with us, you know the Opening Word. Are you intruders?"
"No!" Lem assures him. "We're with you. The Opening Word has, er, slipped our minds."
"We will test you," announces the first twin. "We each have a button on our forearm. Press one and the door will open. Press the other and you will be dealt with. You may ask one of us one question about the button. One of us always tells the truth. The other always lies. You have ten seconds. If you don't press a button, we will know that you are an intruder."

Have faith in Lem, and wait to see what he will do. Go to page 31.
Or, if you don't trust him, leap forward and press a button. Go to page 18.

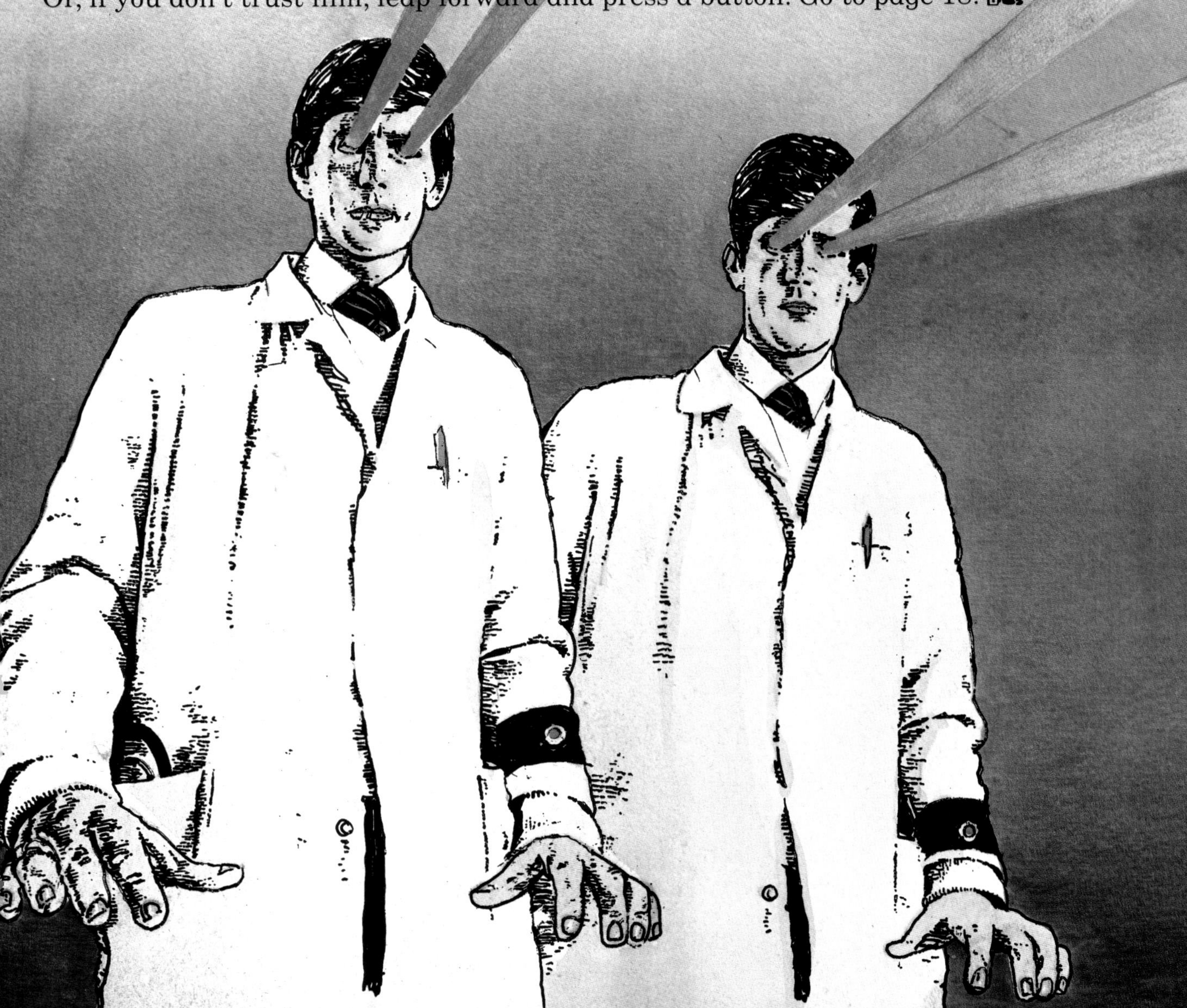

Lem may not look like a secret agent, but he certainly moves like one, gliding smoothly through the wood without a sound.
He wriggles around the last few saplings and stops in front of a massive dead oak. Then he stretches out – and hugs the tree! You are about to run from this madman when you realise that he is twisting some twigs behind the tree. The bark rolls back and you see that the tree is fake.

"Two secret tunnels to the Abbey," Lem explains, pointing. "I'm going by the hard, fast way, but you can take the slow, easy route if you prefer (it leads to the Abbey cloisters). If you go alone, take this ultra-sonic buzzer."

Lem vaults into the hollow tree and rapidly crawls along the narrow tunnel. Follow him to page 27.

Or take the buzzer and enter the slow tunnel alone. Go to page 36.

You creep forward for a closer look – and discover that the 'ghost' is a hologram! "What are you doing here?" someone whispers.

Your hair stands on end. Fear roots you to the spot. "I said, 'What are you doing here?'" the voice hisses angrily. Then its owner steps in front of you. He doesn't look very ghostly, quite solid in fact. You explain about the way into the Abbey. "You must be observant," he remarks. "Perhaps you could be useful. Will you take a message to my partner, Lem?"

"Who are you?" you ask. "What's going on?"

"My name doesn't matter," he replies. "Call me YM3431. I can't divulge my findings, but I'll tell you this: Scotland Yard is very interested in White Monks Abbey!"

YM3431 hands you a map of White Monks Wood and a sealed envelope.

If you want to help him, go to page 4.
Or, if you think that this could be a trap, try to find your friend, Pat, in the wood . Go to page 16.

Two helicopters are hovering overhead, just below roof level. What are they waiting for? A minute passes slowly as you try to squeeze yourself into invisibility behind a dustbin. Then one of the helicopters lands on the platform.

If you have been given a camera, photograph the back of the Abbey. Then, if you think that you have solved the mystery, escape from the Abbey grounds and run to the police station on page 2.
Or, if you think that you need more evidence, enter the Abbey on page 6.

Panting, you look around and see that you are in a dim, dusty corridor. You pass black, cobwebby turnings and rotting doors dangling from broken hinges.

Out of the corner of your eye you see something white flickering against the dirty brown wall. You look up.

A GHOST!

Has it seen you? Surely it can hear your knocking knees and pounding heart. But it doesn't stir.

If you are afraid of ghosts, run through the door behind you to page 42.
Or, if you want to investigate the ghost, go to page 11.

14

The scrunching of gravel under your feet is the only sound as you cross the remains of a drive and take a close look at the front of the Abbey.

Something looks odd, but you're not sure what it is. Before you can decide, the silence is suddenly broken by loud, furious barks. Round the corner of the west tower appears a huge dog.

You're fond of animals, but one glimpse of this one is enough. You take to your heels.

Run to the east tower. Go to page 21.
Or run into the Abbey maze. Go to page 44.
Or run through the archway into the Abbey cloisters. Go to page 36.

The tunnel is clean and dry, but as dark as night. You feel your way until you reach an obstacle. You trace out some sort of control panel raised above the floor. There's a stubby button and something which feels like a lever. You daren't do more than brush the panel with the tips of your fingers, in case you accidentally press the button or trip the lever.

You could try to crawl over the panel, but that would be risky. The ceiling is too low for you to jump over the panel. So what can you do?

Press the button. Go to page 3.

Or pull the lever. Go to page 17.

16

"Pat!" you call, as you gallop into the clearing. "At last!"
"Too right, at last," snaps Pat. "Where have you been?"
You explain.
"Come on," scoffs Pat. "I'm not that gullible. If you must invent weird excuses for being late, you might make them convincing."
"But it's true!" you insist.
"Oh, yes, of course," snorts Pat. "Pull the other one. Now come on. I want to fly my new kite."
You explain and argue until Pat almost believes you. You produce YM3431's letter.
"O.K.," says Pat. "If you're such a terrific detective, what does it say?"

If you can read the message, Pat will be convinced. Lead the way to the Abbey (but don't forget the kite) on page 19.
Or, if you can't work out what YM3431's message means, Pat will never believe you, so start again, on page 1.

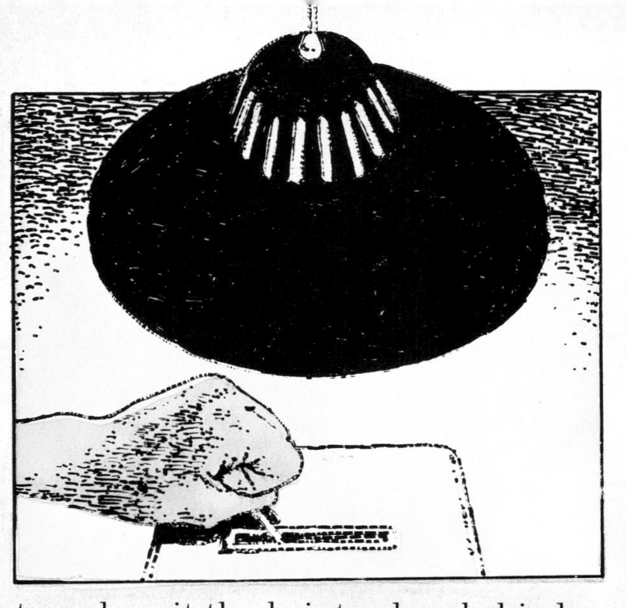

You catch your breath in terror. What if the lever is a booby-trap for intruders? You could be blown into a trillion pieces! You swallow hard and stretch out your shaking hand... You grasp the lever and slowly pull it towards you... An electric light snaps on.

Now that you can see, it's easy to step over the panel and crawl to the end of the tunnel. As you step out of the trap-door, it thuds into place behind you, but you are too stunned to look back. So that's why the rear of the Abbey is so carefully screened by thick trees and bushes! Half of the roof is missing! And the top storey! What are those platforms for? Why is there scaffolding everywhere?

Look for clues at the front of the Abbey on page 14. ☛
Or wait to see what will happen. Go to page 12. ☛

A sudden blow sends you sprawling against the wall. The wall moves, revealing an opening. You stumble through and the wall snaps back into place, leaving you trapped on the other side.

You get to your feet and pound on the false wall. It doesn't move. You can just reach the window ledge, but the bars are too close together for you to climb through.

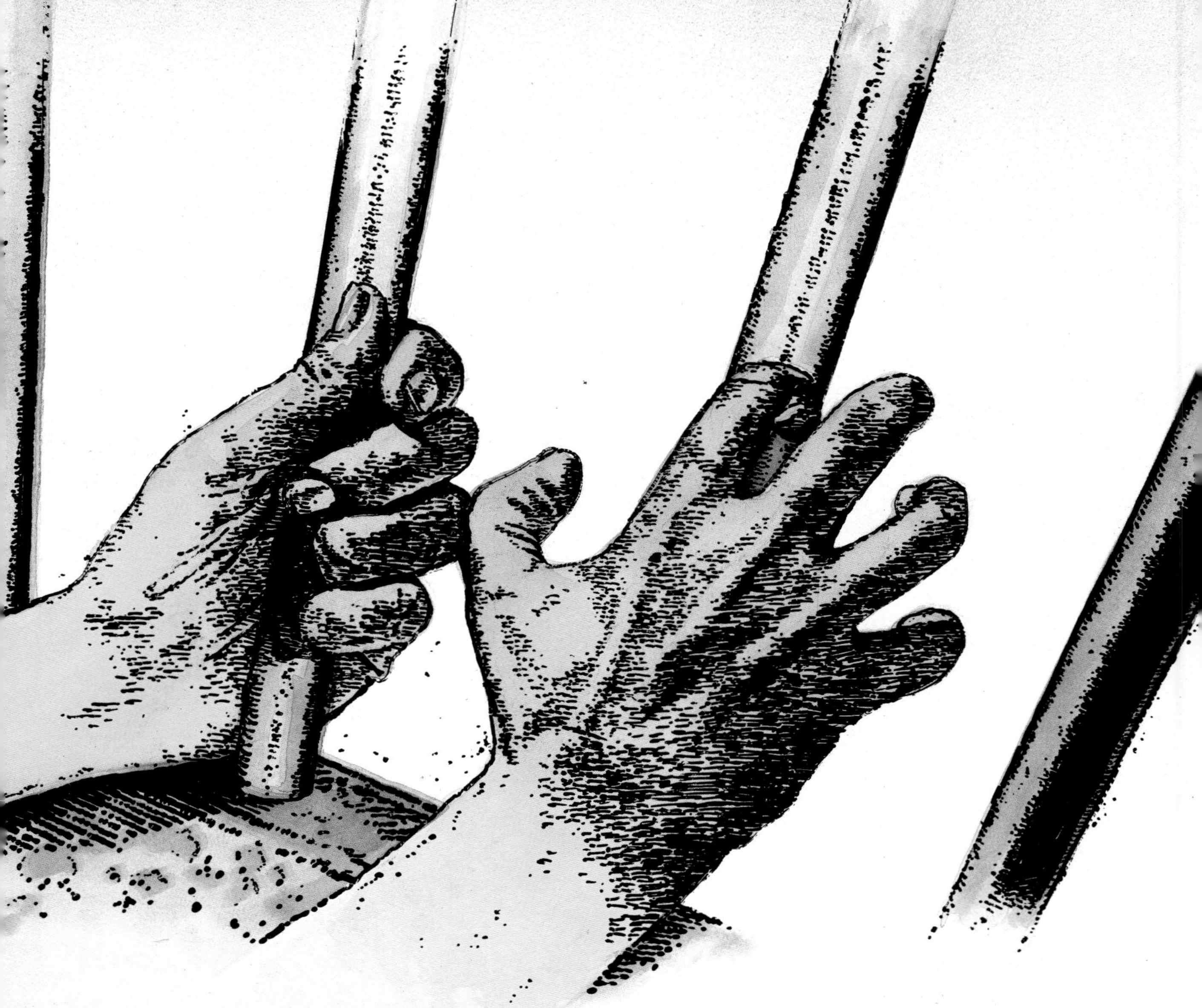

Suddenly, a thin grey cloud hisses through the crack under the door. A muffled voice says, "O.K., Boss. I've fixed it. That gas would put an elephant to sleep in five minutes. When the busybody wakes up, we'll be gone."

You have less than five minutes. If you have a kite, stretch up and push it through the window, tying the string to a bar. Hope for a stiff breeze and go to page 45.
Or, if you don't have a kite, risk the gas and go to page 26.

Scouting around the side of the Abbey, you spot a small window. It's open and, thanks to last term's high-jump practice, you can vault through.

You are in a long, draughty corridor lined with suits of armour and old weapons. Suddenly, you hear a door slam in the distance. The carpet rises on the gusty floor and an icy blast chills your face. Someone's coming.

Hide, quickly! Leap into one of the suits of armour.

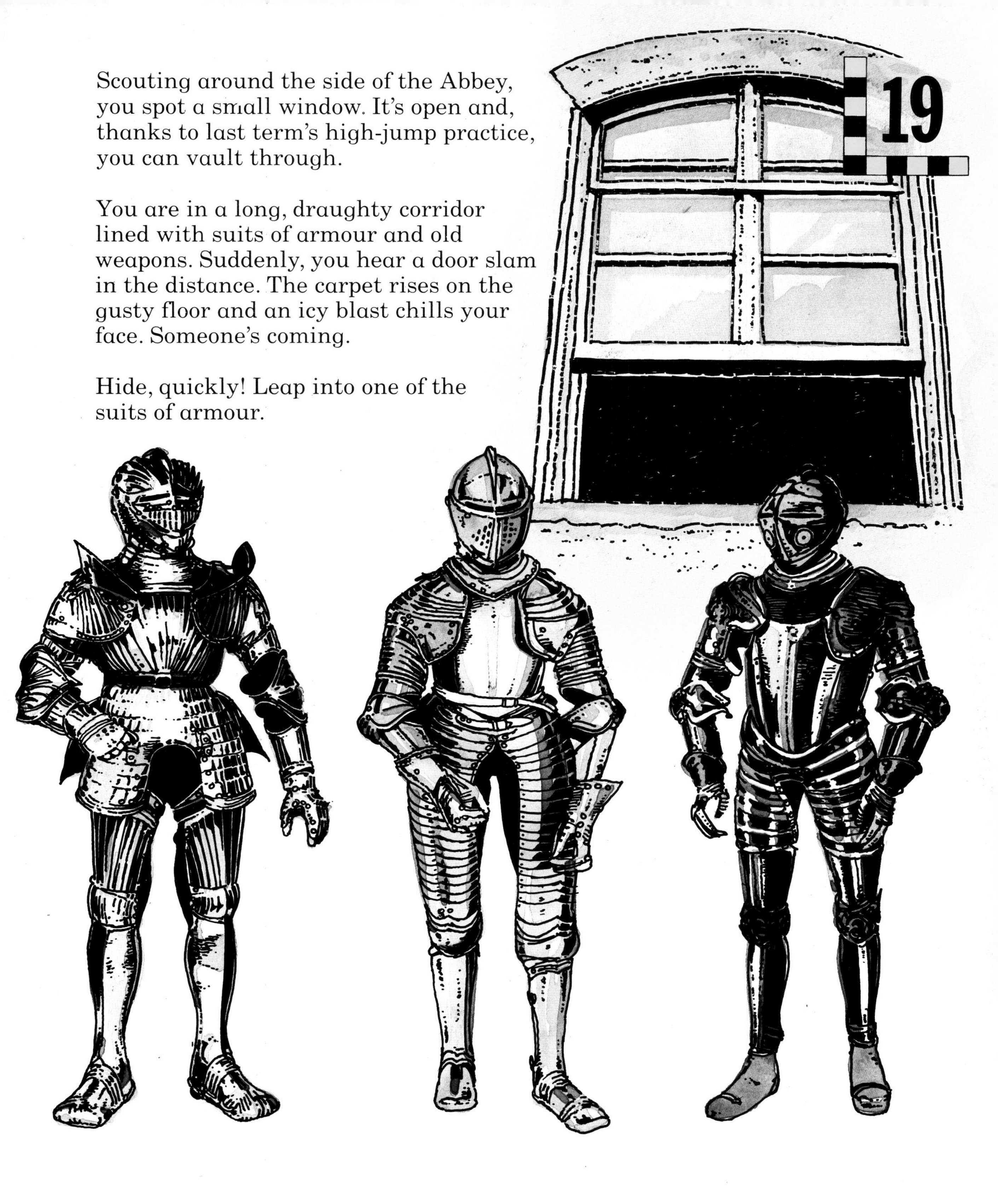

If you choose the first suit of armour, go to page 29.
Or, if you choose the second suit of armour, go to page 23.
Or, if you choose the third suit of armour, go to page 40.

20

You're trapped!
"Don't try to escape," orders Meat Cleaver. "You've nowhere to run! Where are your friends?"
"I don't know what you're talking about," you say defiantly.

"Oh, don't you?" Meat Cleaver snarls. "How did you get in here then? Who are you working for? What do you know?"

You bluff desperately. "I came to get my kite. It was blown in and I want it back."
"A likely story," sneers Meat Cleaver. "Never fear. The Boss will make you talk soon enough!"

Meat Cleaver drags you along the corridor, your heels bumping on the rough stone, to page 41.
Or, if you have a buzzer, secretly turn it on and go to page 43.

You sprint around the side of the east tower, hoping to lose the dog in the shrubbery. Then you see that your way is blocked – and the dog is closing in!

Pounding past the ivy-covered walls, you see an open window ahead. Can you run in a straight line until the very last minute and then hurl yourself sideways through the window? Perhaps the dog won't be able to stop in time.

Wait until the animal is almost upon you, then scramble through the window to page 13.
Or brave its jaws and double back. Try to enter the Abbey via the secret tunnel on page 15.

22

The corridor leads to a big, old-fashioned kitchen. The walls are festooned with cobwebs. Grease and grime cover every surface. It looks deserted but the ashes on the hearth are warm. You'd better go. Someone has been here and they could be back at any moment.

Suddenly, that someone appears in the doorway. He has a wicked-looking meat cleaver and a wicked-looking grin.

Run! Get out of the kitchen and along the corridor as fast as you can. Meat Cleaver is in hot pursuit! Turn into a side corridor by going to page 24.
Or run out of the Abbey and find the police by going to page 25.
Or keep running along the main corridor by going to page 20.

Spying through the eye-slits of the helmet, you see two men walking towards you, deep in conversation. Luckily they don't look at the suits. One of them is carrying a sheaf of papers. As he walks past, a sheet flutters to your steel-covered feet.

When the men are out of sight, you peel off the armour and snatch up the paper. It's some sort of diagram. Mazes! It's a plan of several, slightly different mazes. Could this be a clue to the mystery?

You tuck the paper into your sleeve. If you think that it might be a useful piece of evidence, hurry to the police on page 2.
Or, if you still have YM3431's message, go back to White Monks Wood and hunt for Lem on page 4.
Or investigate the Abbey maze on page 44.

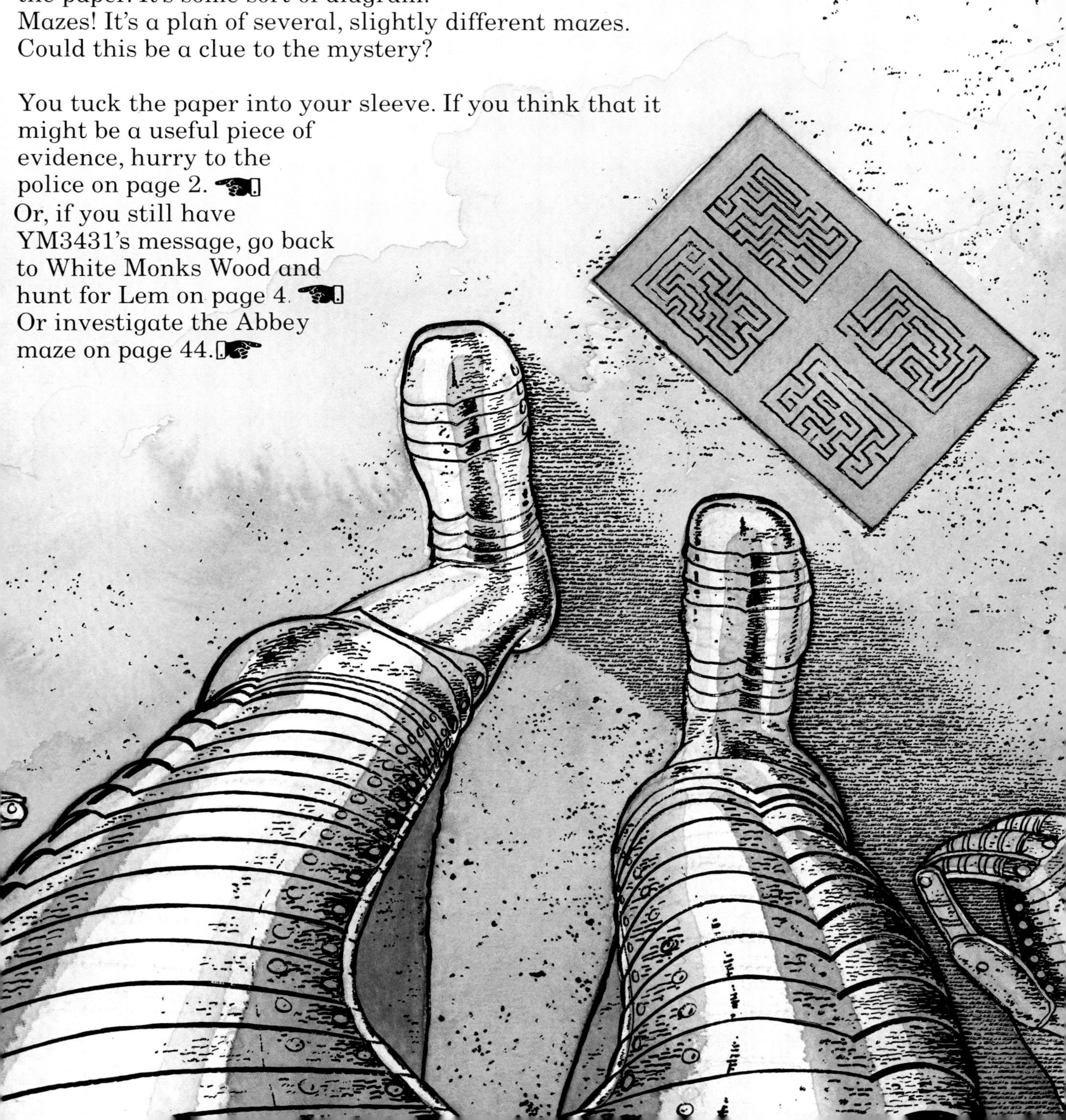

24

A dead end! Lurching round the corner comes Meat Cleaver, grinning evilly. He paces slowly towards you, smiling and lifting the long blade.

You're too tired to run. Is this the end? Too exhausted to care, you slump against the wall. Three sections of panelling slide away, revealing three chutes. No time to investigate them. Select one and dive in.

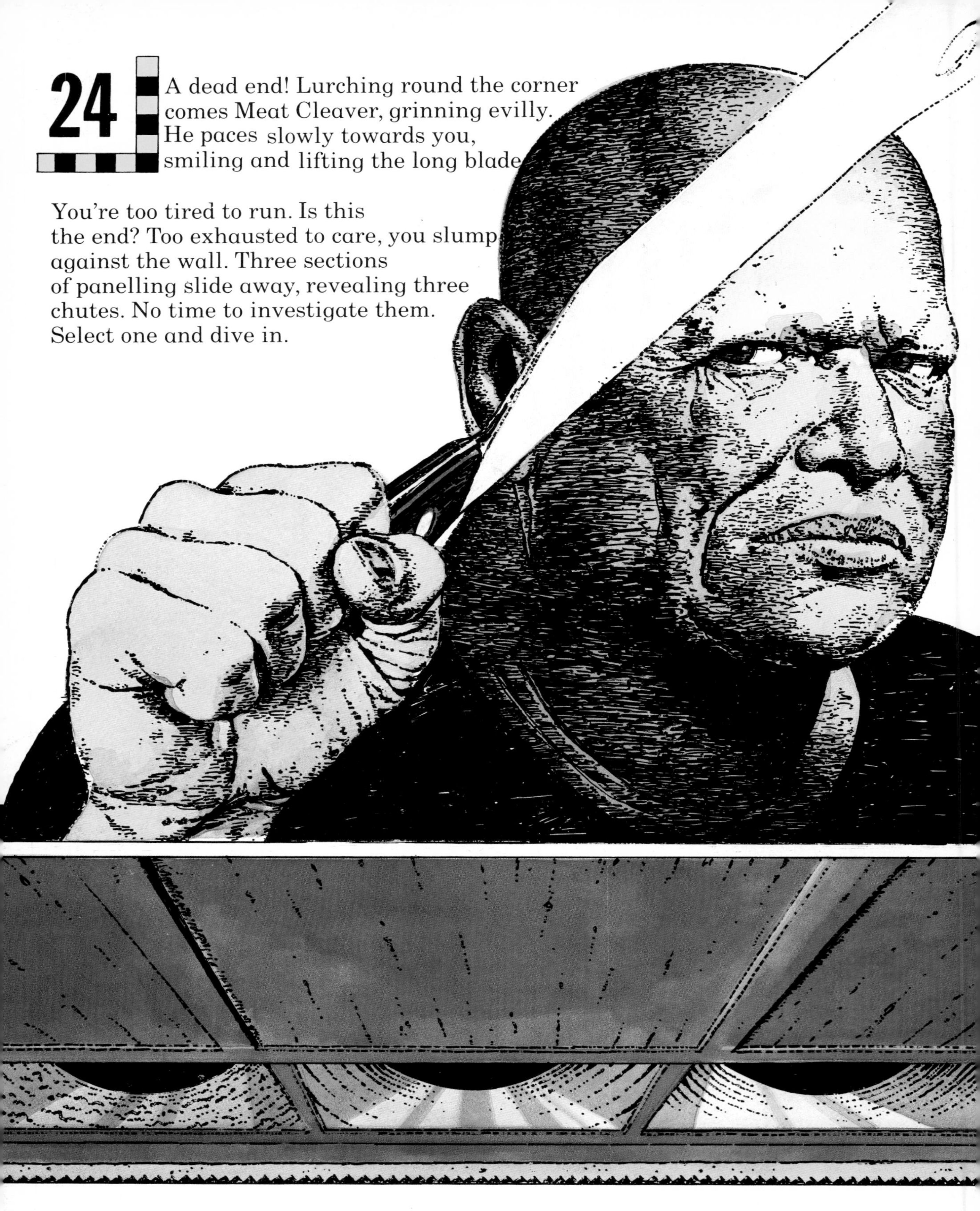

Choose the first chute and slide down to page 6.
Or choose the second and go to page 7.
Or slither down the third to come out at page 34.

You arrive at the police station. "The Abbey!" you gasp. "A mystery at..."
"Oh yes?" enquires the sergeant. "A new game is it? Practical joke?"
You try to explain.
"White Monks Abbey is private property," the policeman says wearily. "It's no place for hide-and-seek. If you saw anything in the grounds, it was the new owner. He's renovating the old ruin they tell me."
"No," you insist. "A sinister plot..."
"Run along now," sighs the policeman.

Go back to the Abbey. If you haven't used it before, you'll find a secret tunnel in the wood on page 15. ☛
Or, if you have used the tunnel before, go to the front of the Abbey on page 14. ☛
Or find your way through the shrubbery. Go to page 19. ☛

26

You wake up feeling dazed and confused.
"Oh, Mum, it's not time to get up yet, is it?" you groan.
Then you realise that you're not at home.
You're in a dark, gloomy dungeon.
With a groan, you shake your head and stagger to the door.
It's open. Thank heavens!

You climb to the ground floor.
Every room you pass is deserted and empty.
The Abbey really does look as if no one has been inside for ten years.

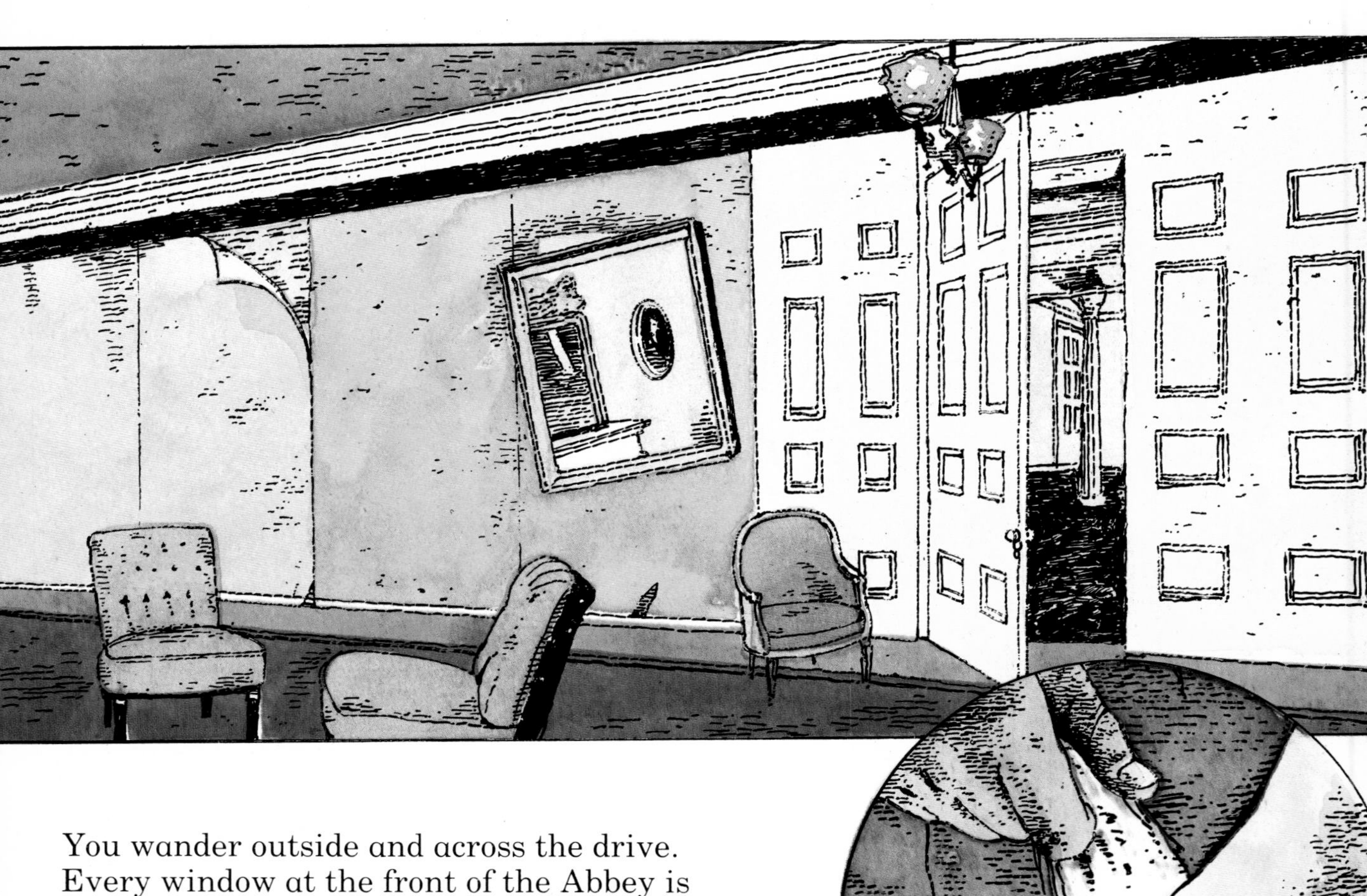

You wander outside and across the drive. Every window at the front of the Abbey is smashed. The barbed wire is torn and flapping and the tunnel exit has vanished. Who would believe your story? You try to remember. Didn't you have some evidence? Eagerly you search through your pockets. Empty!

Time to go home. Perhaps you'll find another mystery to investigate soon.

You catch up with Lem in the secret passage. When you reach the Abbey he cautiously lifts a trap door and peers out. "No one about," he says. "Come up and keep quiet. No sign of YM3431. If he had time, he'll have left a message."

You scour the room. Then, forgetting to be silent, yell, "Look! On the mirror!"
"Ah, code plus three, a simple cipher," whispers Lem. "He must have been in a hurry. Can you read it?"

If you can understand YM3431's message, help Lem to find him.
Go to page 9. ☛
Or, if you can't decode the message, Lem will send you home.
Start again on page 1. ☛
Or go back to White Monks Wood on page 16. ☛
Or look at the map on the last page of the book.
It might give you a clue about the code… ☛

You look at the portrait very carefully.
Yes, the eyes aren't painted, they're real!
Suddenly the eyes are gone. You see a piece of canvas slide back into place.

Before you can get away, someone grabs you from behind. You are dragged, screaming and kicking, out of the door.

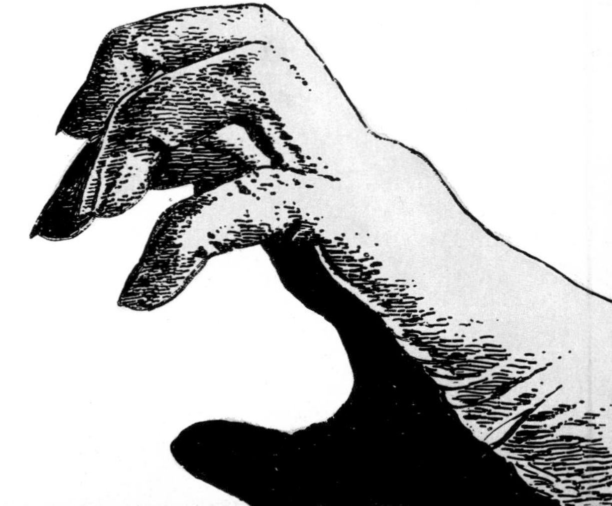

If you have an ultra-sonic buzzer, turn it on now. Go to page 43. ☞
Or you'll be carried off to page 41. ☞

The instant you are settled inside the armour, the wall behind you revolves, taking armour – and you – with it! Peering through the helmet, you see a long, dimly lit corridor. The coast is clear, but who keeps the light burning? You wonder where you are as you clamber out of the armour. You remove the steel plates gingerly, lowering them to the floor with great care, terrified that the clanking of metal will give you away.

You tip-toe away towards a green baize door.

If you have been inside the Abbey for hours, go through the door to page 22.
Or, if you are still fresh enough to explore the Abbey some more, continue along the main corridor and find the room on page 34

You pause to rest on the parapet. Why don't the helicopters land? Far below,you can see the Abbey maze. It's easy to trace the way out from up here. Suddenly you see that the hedges are moving! Workmen are carrying them to new positions.

Ah ha! The maze is planted in camouflaged tubs, so that the pattern can be changed easily. Why? Could it be a way of sending secret messages? Perhaps a way of communicating with someone in the air – with helicopter pilots? It would be better than radio, because no one could listen in.

Observe the new layout of the maze. If you have a camera, photograph it.

Take your evidence to the police on page 25.
Or try to find Lem and YM3431 inside the Abbey on page 24.

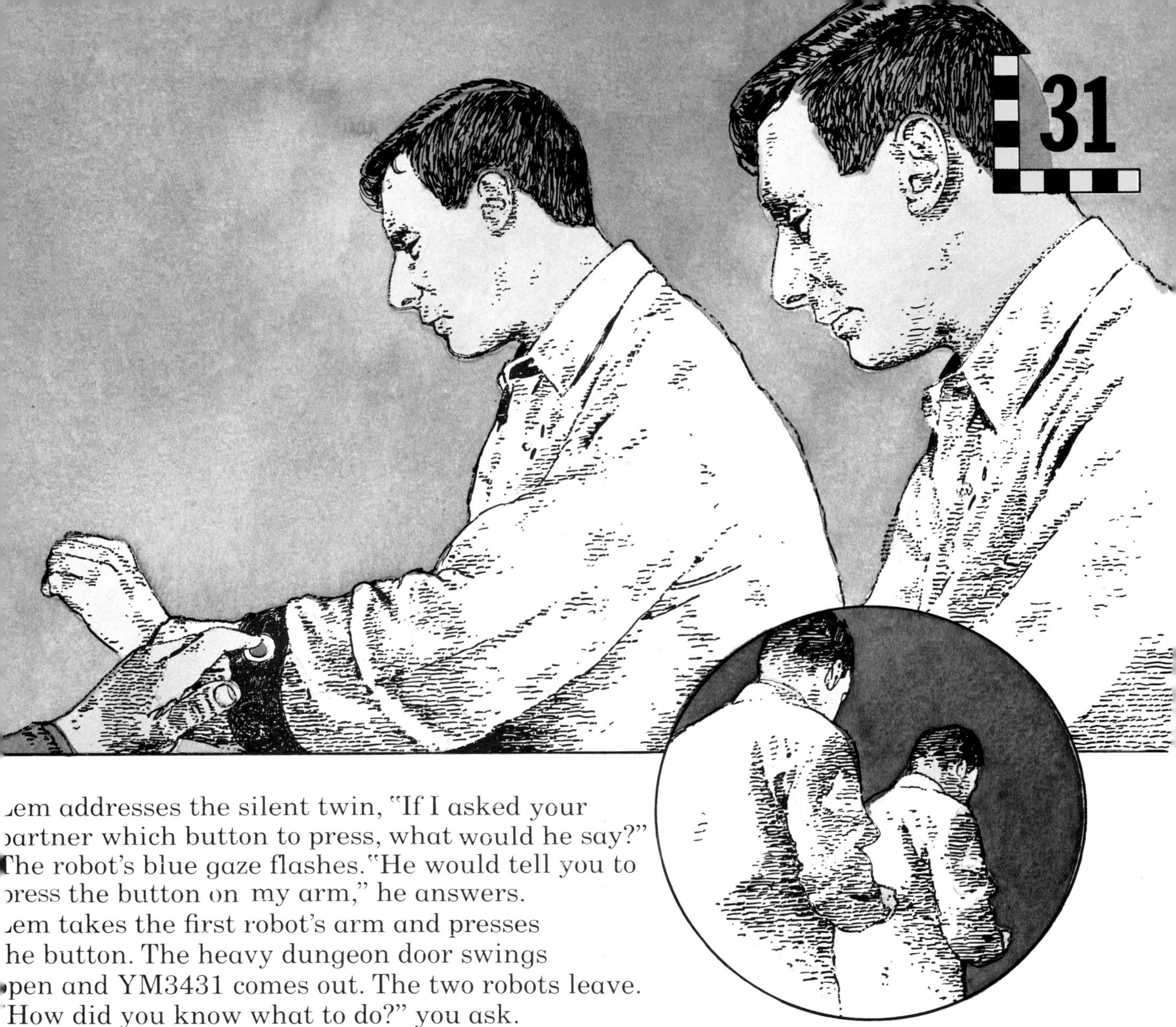

Lem addresses the silent twin, "If I asked your partner which button to press, what would he say?" The robot's blue gaze flashes. "He would tell you to press the button on my arm," he answers.
Lem takes the first robot's arm and presses the button. The heavy dungeon door swings open and YM3431 comes out. The two robots leave.
"How did you know what to do?" you ask.
"Well," replies Lem, "if one robot always lies and the other always tells the truth, if I ask one what the other would say, the answer will be always be wrong, won't it?"
You decide to work that out later. Meanwhile you ask, "What's going on?"

"A sinister plot," YM3431 tells you. "The Boss of a criminal organisation plans to kidnap world leaders and replace them with robots! He's quite mad, of course."

If you have found some evidence to prove what YM3431 said, he will move in. Radio for police reinforcements, go to page 8.
Or, if you don't have enough evidence, split up and search. Try the corridor on page 22.

The Enemy shoves you through a door. "Hah!" roars a thin pasty-faced man. You spies are always trying to infiltrate White Monks."
"I'm not a ..." you begin, but the Boss interrupts, "Oh no, you didn't microfilm my robot blueprints. You didn't bamboozle my guardian robots. You didn't send my robot dog crashing into a wall – oh no!" You listen hard, trying not to betray your amazement.

"Admit it – I know everything!" rants the Boss. "No junior spy can prevent my robots from replacing world leaders and taking over the world! Robot, deal with this intruder!"

The Enemy robot pushes you through the door. If you have been given a buzzer, turn it on and go to page 43.
Or, if you don't have a buzzer, go to page 18.

This way leads you around and around, back and forward until you are dizzy. When you finally find a gap in one of the hedge walls, you have completely lost your sense of direction.

As you squeeze through the hole, you see that you are back in White Monks Wood. You're exhausted, hot and dazed, so you lean against a tree to think things over.

You could give up, go home, and forget White Monks Abbey.
Or you could drag your sore feet to the police station on page 25.

This must be the old ballroom. Imagine the days when grand balls were held here. It must have been brilliantly lit by huge, glittering chandeliers. Orchestras would have played all night and the women's sumptuous gowns would have swept the floor as they twirled and span.

You must have a vivid imagination. You can almost hear people waltzing towards you...in fact, you can hear them! Gulp! You edge backwards. The steps follow. Thump, bump-bump, THUMP, bump-bump, bump, bump, bump, THUD, bump-bump-bump...but there's no one there!

The floor beneath your feet suddenly gives a little hop. One by one the loose old boards lift, creaking, as the invisible dancers pass by. HELP!

Run for your life to page 6.
Or be as brave as you can and investigate the ghostly waltzers on page 37.

Easy-peasy! You're obviously heading directly for the centre of the maze. From there it'll be a cinch to find your way ou-OU-OUCH!

The maze is booby-trapped and you're the booby! You have fallen into a pit!

A shadow falls across the hole as someone stands on the lip. "Caught!" he chortles triumphantly.
The Enemy is carrying a gas cylinder and hose. Think quickly! If you can invent a good reason for him to take you to his leader, say it now and perhaps you'll be able to escape on the way. Go to page 41.☞
Or, if you think that the Enemy Boss will be worse than the Enemy, wake up on page 26. ☜

36

You creep through the eerie cloisters, looking at the rusty old weapons which line the walls. A pikestaff or sword might come in handy in this place, but you decide that they are too heavy for you to lift down. You turn away – and narrowly avoid being split in half! The pike has torn itself from its mounting and toppled to the floor, on the spot where you stood a second ago!

You tell yourself that it is just coincidence. A rusty old hook must have snapped. Then every weapon on the long wall begins to jerk up and down. One by one they tear themselves away from the wall and throw themselves at you.

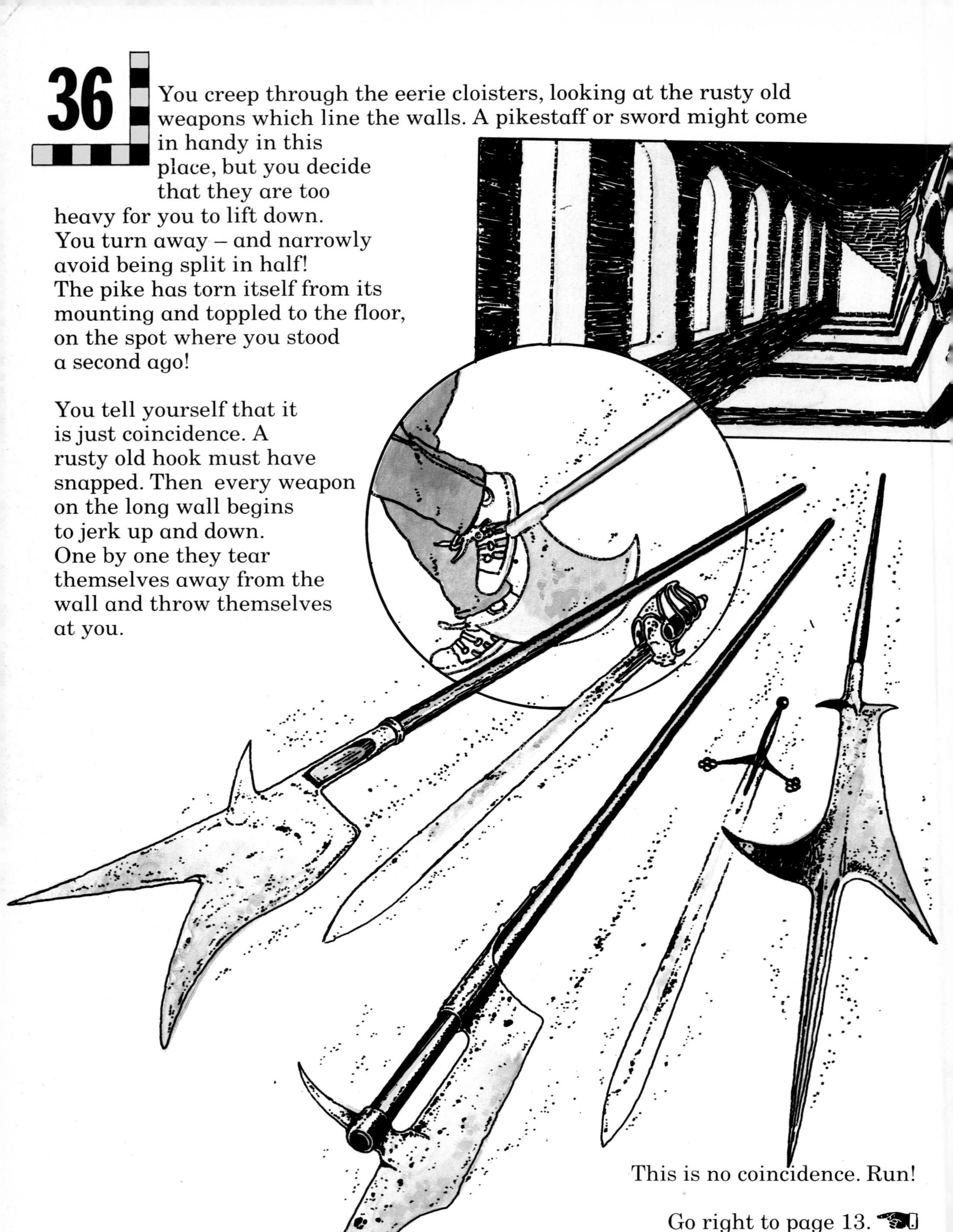

This is no coincidence. Run!

Go right to page 13.
Or left to page 42.

You dash out of the room. No one in the corridor. You run back. Silence. Firmly telling yourself that there are no such things as ghosts, you prise up a floorboard. Underneath you find a pulley with a taut metal string leading under the floor. When the string is plucked, the springy board creaks. When you lift the next board, you are not surprised to see a tiny loudspeaker nestling below.

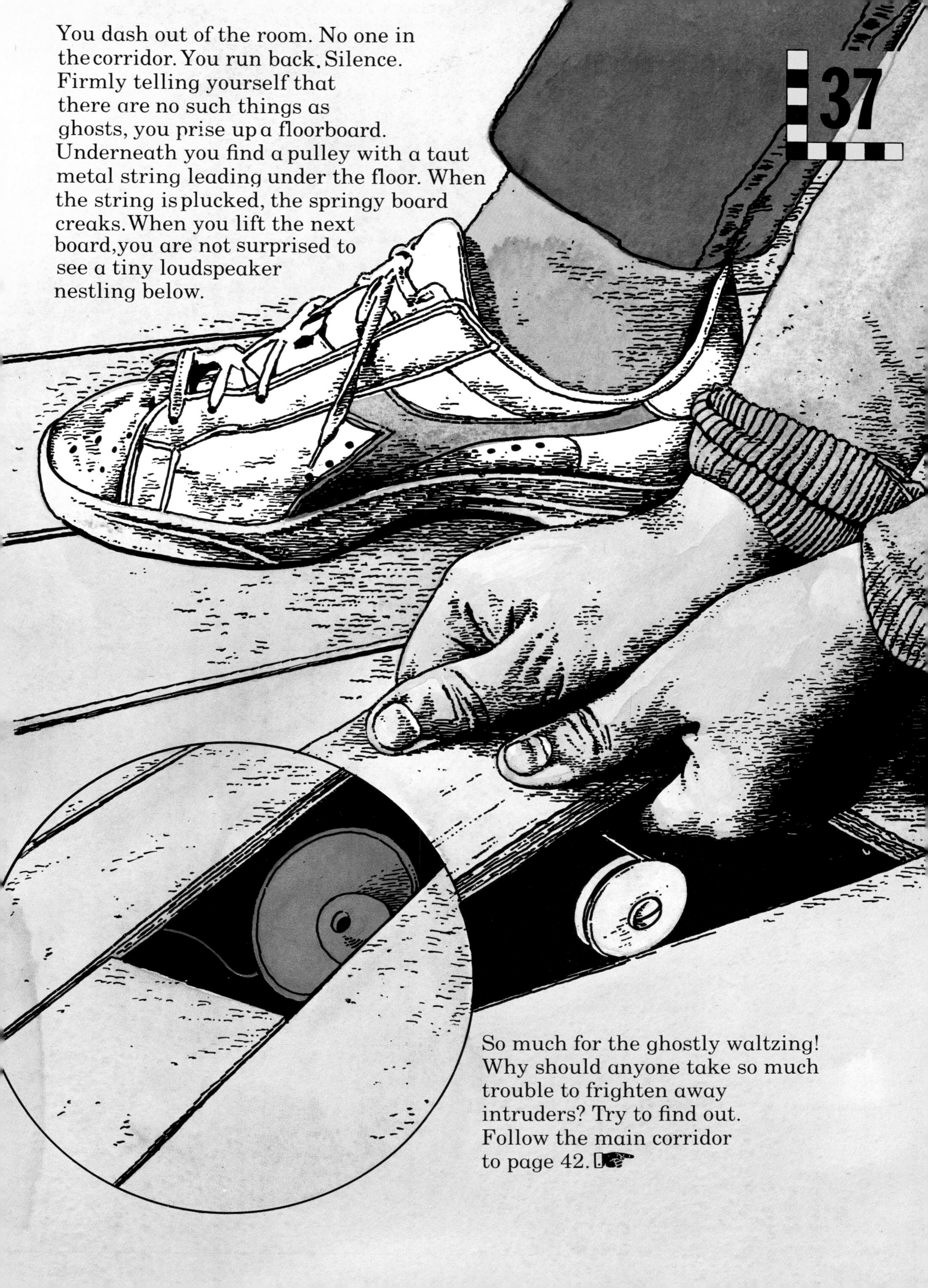

So much for the ghostly waltzing! Why should anyone take so much trouble to frighten away intruders? Try to find out.

Follow the main corridor to page 42.

38

This way leads left, right, left, straight ahead, back to where you started from, right – and to a dead end.

Brr, it's getting cold. You huddle down in the corner, exhausted. Gradually you nod off to sleep. You don't hear the footsteps trudging heavily along the maze avenues, but you wake up when someone lifts your head to tie a mask over your mouth.

It's the Enemy! If you have an ultra-sonic buzzer, turn it on now and go to page 43.
Or, if you don't have a buzzer, go to page 26.

Lem leads you to the back of the Abbey where two helicopters are hovering at roof level.

"Another delivery – I wonder who..." Lem gasps. "I must find YM3431 at once. Take this micro camera and get some photographs for evidence. I'll be back in twenty minutes. If I don't make it, fetch the police."

Pointing a long metal tube at the Abbey roof, he adds, "I'll give you a better view." Something darts upwards. You hear the rasp of metal on stone. Craning your neck, you see a rope ladder dangling from a grappling iron. Lem hurries away.

Will you climb the ladder?
Then go to page 5.
Or will you creep from dustbin to dustbin and climb the ivy on the side wall? Then go to page 30.

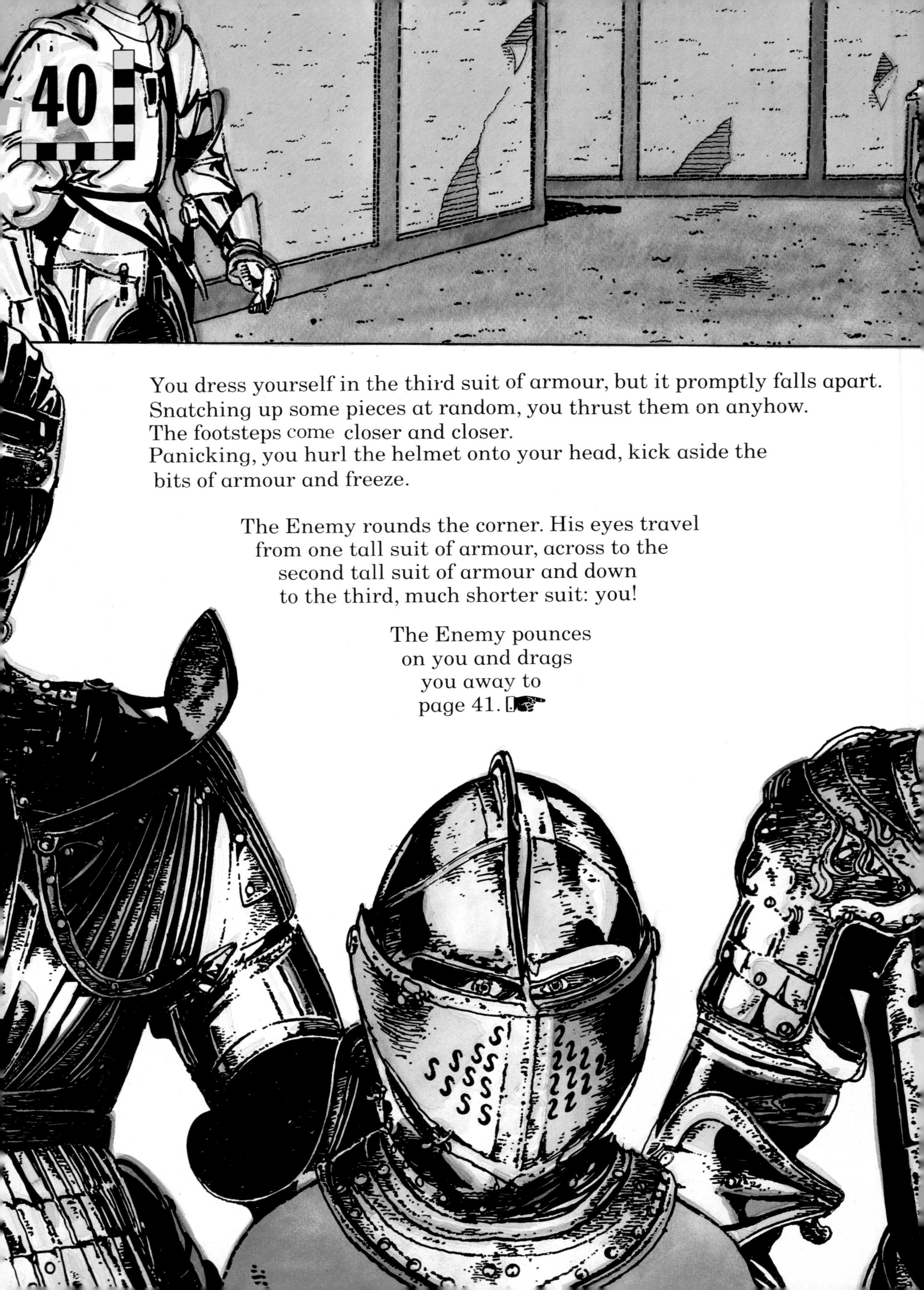

You dress yourself in the third suit of armour, but it promptly falls apart. Snatching up some pieces at random, you thrust them on anyhow. The footsteps come closer and closer.
Panicking, you hurl the helmet onto your head, kick aside the bits of armour and freeze.

The Enemy rounds the corner. His eyes travel from one tall suit of armour, across to the second tall suit of armour and down to the third, much shorter suit: you!

The Enemy pounces on you and drags you away to page 41.

How can you get away? The Enemy is huge and powerful. His muscles look like solid steel. In fact, they probably are solid steel. You rack your brains frantically. Suddenly an ear-splitting clanging makes you both start. The Enemy's grip loosens.

Tear away and find your way out of the Abbey to the police station on page 25.

Or, if you want to learn more about the secret of the Abbey, let the Enemy grab you again and go with him to page 32.

You come to a long, low room. The walls are hung with grimy old portraits. You intend to hurry past without looking at them, but one attracts your attention. It is brighter than the others, perhaps newer. Its eyes seem to follow you. Silly, but portraits always give you that feeling. Of course it's all nonsense. Or is it?

If you want to take a closer look at the portrait, go to page 28. ☞
Or, if you don't think it's safe to stand still anywhere in White Monks Abbey, run out into the corridor on page 24. ☞

Saved! In the nick of time, Lem bursts in yelling, "Put your hands up!" You stand behind him. "I've had to blow my cover and call in police reinforcements," he tells you. "Have you found any evidence which could help?"

If you have any evidence, meet the police in White Monks Wood. Go to page 8.
Or, if you don't have any evidence, Lem will send you home. You won't see him and his partner, YM3431, round up the criminal gang. Never mind, you have helped to solve the mystery of White Monks Abbey.

44

You try to memorise the path you take through the maze, but the rows of tall hedges all look the same. Soon you have to admit that you are hopelessly lost. You leap up and down, trying to look over the hedges, but you can't see any way out. Ahead you see three avenues. One leads left, one right and one straight ahead.

Follow the avenue to the left on page 38.
Or follow the avenue to the right on page 33.
Or follow the avenue straight ahead on page 35.

"Are you there?" hisses a familiar voice.
"Yes, it's me," you whisper. "Get me out!"
You hear something scratching and scuffling at the lock. Then the door swings open and you step out.
"Thanks, YM3431," you begin. "Glad you saw..."
"Shh," YM3431 interrupts. "Quiet!"
YM3431 leads the way to a concealed trap-door, through a cramped, twisting shaft, up into a hollow tree and out into the wood.
"This is where we say 'goodbye'," he tells you. "I can't waste time rescuing you, so I'm going back to the Abbey and you're going home." He leaps back into the tree and, closing the bark door, calls, "Don't try to follow me. By tonight everything will have gone."
Home will seem very dull after White Monks Abbey.

46
ZKLWH PRQNV DEEHB